KU-397-689

This book belongs to

...............................

# At the ZOO

by Mary Atkinson

Can you find
a ladybird on
every page?

make
believe
ideas

# Get the most from this reader

•••••••••••••••••••••••••••••••••••••

**Before reading:**

● Look at the pictures and discuss
  them together. Ask questions such as,
  "What is the hippo doing?"

● Relate the topic to your child's world.
  For example, say: "What animals did
  we see at the zoo?"

● Familiarise your child with book
  vocabulary by using terms such as
  *word, letter, title, author* and *text*.

•••••••••••••••••••••••••••••••••••••

**During reading:**

● Prompt your child to sound out unknown words.
  Draw attention to neglected middle or
  end sounds.

● Encourage your child to use the pictures as
  clues to unknown words.

● Occasionally, ask what might happen next,
  and then check together as you read on.

● Monitor your child's understanding. Repeated readings can improve fluency and comprehension.

● Keep reading sessions short and enjoyable. Stop if your child becomes tired or frustrated.

• • • • • • • • • • • • • • • • • • • • • • • • • • • • • • • • • •

**After reading:**

● Discuss the book. Encourage your child to form opinions with questions such as, "What did you like best about this book?"

● Help your child work through the fun activities at the back of the book. Then ask him or her to reread the story. Praise any improvement.

# Tom sees a lion.

"Lions lie in the sun," says Tom.

9

Tom sees a zebra.

"Zebras run and kick," says Tom.

11

Tom sees a tiger.

"Tigers hide in the trees," says Tom.

13

# Tom sees a polar bear.

"Polar bears live in the snow," says Tom.

15

Tom sees a hippo.

"Hippos like to sleep," says Tom.

17

Tom sees a monkey.

"What do monkeys do?" asks Tom.

19

The monkey takes
Tom's glasses.

"Monkeys wear glasses!" says Tom.

# Discussion Questions

1. Can you name two animals that Tom sees?

2. Which animal is asleep?

3. What other animals might you see at the zoo?

# ♨ Sight Words ♨

Learning sight words helps you
read fluently. Practise these
sight words from the book.
Use them in sentences of your own.

in

like

run

the

at

do

see

say

# ✏ Rhyming Words ✏

Can you find the rhyming pairs?
Say them aloud.

sun

hide

side

tree

bee

bun

keep

mow

pick

sleep

kick

snow

# Writing Practice

Read the words, and then
trace them with your finger.

zebra

ask

bear

hippo

monkey

glasses

27

# ~ Silly Sentences ~

Have fun filling in the gap in each sentence. Use the ideas below or make up your own.

## Tom sees a ...........................

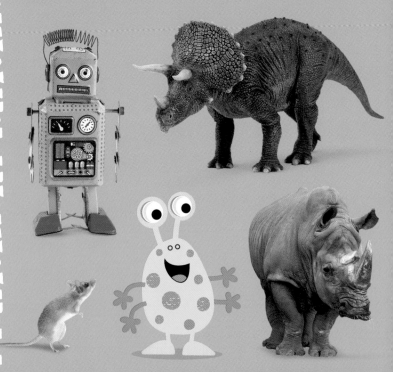

"Flamingoes like to .............,"
says Tom.